Contemporary Monologues for Kids & Teens

Kerry Kazmierowizctrimm

A Beat by Beat Book
bbbpress.com

Published by Beat by Beat Press
bbbpress.com
Copyright © 2022 by Kerry Kazmierowizctrimm

Manufactured in the United States of America

ISBN: 979-8-9850795-1-7

*Dedicated to
June, Suzanne,
& Getty.*

INTRODUCTION

These monologues are generally intended for actors aged 7 to 14, but no specific ages are put on any of them; just the find the one that excites you and have fun!

The characters have been written to be played by any gender. Pronouns have been assigned to characters addressed within the monologues, but feel free to change these as desired. If you want to change "Dad" to "Mom," or a brother to a sister or simply a sibling, feel free! These monologues are intended to capture feelings that people of any gender and background can experience.

Also, many of these monologues mention who the character is speaking to. Since it's a monologue, you won't be performing it with another actor onstage, but I wanted to let you know what your relationship is with the unseen character, so you can start to think about how that might impact the way you perform the monologue. Do you talk with your mom the same way you talk with your best friend? Probably not, so how does that impact the moment?

I hope you have as much fun performing these monologues as I had writing them!

Kerry Kazmierowicztrimm

TABLE OF CONTENTS

MONOLOGUES

COUNTING SHEEP

Devon talks to Mrs. Campbell.

DEVON

Mrs. Campbell, I can explain. You know how at night you're supposed to count little sheep in your head until you fall asleep? I do that, and I almost fall asleep, but then I think, "Hey. How are all these sheep gonna get to sleep? Do they count little people in their heads until *they* fall asleep?" And then I think, "Hey! What if I'm just a little person in a big sheep's head? What if my parents, my best friend, and even you, Mrs. Campbell, are all inside a sheep's head, getting counted over and over and over again until the sheep finally falls asleep?" And *then* I think, "HEY! What happens when the sheep <u>does</u> fall asleep?! Will I still exist, or am I just gonna disappear to make room for sweet, happy sheep dreams?!" I stay up all night thinking about that. And *that's* why I fell asleep in your class, Mrs. Campbell. So, when you think about it, it's actually the sheep's fault. Not mine.

CAST LIST

Sidney, a child theatre critic, steps forward.

SIDNEY

Stand back, everyone, stand back! Yes, yes, I know you've been waiting for hours for the cast list to go up, but as our school's number-one and only theatre critic, it is only right that I see it first. Who else has seen six of Ms. Meier's previous productions and can offer brilliant insights into her casting process? NO ONE! Now, let me see...

(Sidney looks at the cast list.)

Jessica as the evil countess? Interesting. It may seem like an odd choice, but when you think about how intense she gets during kickball, it makes a lot of sense.

(keeps reading the list, then shocked)

Nathan as Prince Charming? Nathan?! At lunch today, he burped the entire alphabet! To say he will need to lose himself in the role is an *understatement*.

(to Nathan)

No offense, Nathan. And congrats!

(Sidney looks at the cast list again.)

Alright, who else?

(reads:)

Toby as Tree Number Four, yep.

Devon as the Grandfather, that's fair, he is almost *twelve*.

An Assistant Director? Well, that's different. Ms. Meier never brought on an Assistant Director before. I wonder who could possibly fill such an important role.

(reads his/her name)

It's...it's me. It's me! I'm the Assistant Director!!! How did Ms. Meier know that directing has always been my dream?! This is the best day ever! And we will have the best SHOW ever! Ms. Meier and I will make sure the whole cast is amazing! Even you, Nathan! Now, let's make some ART! WOO!!!

2

BURNING BRIGHT

Morgan stands outside, under the stars, talking to his/her younger sibling.

MORGAN

Come here, bud. I want to show you something.
    (points to the sky)
Look at all those stars. Burning bright. Shining down on all of us. Sharing their beauty. And their light. Well, the thing is, those stars are trillions and trillions and trillions of miles away. So, it takes a long time for their beauty to reach us. So long, that some of those stars are already gone. They don't exist anymore. But even though they're gone, we still get to see their beauty. And take comfort in their light...I know you miss Grandma. So do I. But her light still burns. Every time Mom smiles. And whenever you laugh. I see her light shining through. I hope you can, too.

SEEDS

Jordan comes forward holding a bag of pumpkin seeds.

JORDAN

Taylor? Hey. Hi. Sorry to bother you, but I, um, I got you something.

(holds up the bag)

They're seeds. Pumpkin seeds. I, um, I was gonna get you flowers - those long ones, what are they called? *Lilies* - but then, when I got to the store, I picked them up - the lilies - and I saw that they were already starting to...um...what's the word? *Wilt.* They were starting to wilt. And I was like, "Why would I get Taylor something that's dying?" That just seems, I dunno, sad. And when I see you, sad isn't how I feel. Not ever. So it just, it didn't feel right. To get you flowers. But as I was leaving the store, I saw these pumpkin seeds. And when I think about seeds, I think about...about possibility. What might be. If you plant them and...and...what's the word? *Nurture* them. Help them grow. So, yeah, I got you these seeds. As a way of saying that I like...I like...I like...

(almost says "you," but instead:)

Pumpkins. I like pumpkins. And wanted to see if you might like pumpkins, too.

(offers the bag)

So? Do you like them?

SCARY

Aspen is in the process of telling a scary story.

ASPEN

MASSIVE! This beast was MASSIVE. It had pitch-black eyes and sharp, sharp teeth. It was the scariest thing I'd ever seen. And because I'd walked back to the car to grab my jacket, I was alone. All alone with this *monster*. No one to save me. If I was gonna survive, I had to come with a plan *fast*. And so...I screamed.
   (To demonstrate, Aspen screams and strikes a big, intimidating pose.)
I screamed at this monster! As loud as I could! So it would know that it couldn't mess with me!
   (Drops the pose.)
But then...it did something that I wasn't expecting. It froze. And fell on its side. I had scared it so bad that it fainted - or worse. And the thing is, a moment ago, I thought that if I did scare it, I'd feel so tough. But I didn't. I just felt bad. Cuz it didn't look so big anymore. Or scary.

And that's when I realized...*I* was the scary one. My heart hurt. I could actually *feel* my heart hurting. I ran into the house, to get water and food and whatever else this creature might need, but by the time I got back, it was gone. It had run off. To save itself from the big, scary monster. From me.

When I told my dad about the creature, he said it sounded like an opossum. People are scared of them because of how they look. Well, I don't want to be scared of them anymore. Or any other poor animal that's probably more scared of me than I am of them. And that's why I'm here. I'm hoping you'll let me volunteer at your animal shelter.

SURPRISE

Ari stands next to a crib, looking at his/her baby sister.

ARI

So. Lee. You're my sister. My baby sister. Never had a sister. Never wanted a sister. But then one day, my parents - oh, I guess I mean "our parents," *ugh* - were like, "Surprise, Ari! You're getting a baby sister!" Surprises are supposed to be *good* things. Like ice-cream cake. Or toys. And not to be mean, Lee, but you are nothing like ice-cream cake. Or even a toy. My parents - or, okay, *our* parents - were like, "Now, Ari, don't pick up Lee. Don't roll Lee across the floor. Don't bounce Lee like a basketball." Then what am I supposed to do with you?! I mean, you're a part of this family now, but all you do is lie there and stare at me and drool and...

(reacting to something)

Wait. No. Don't cry. No, no, no, please don't cry! Cuz when you cry, it makes my heart hurt, and I...I...

(feeling something unexpected)

...I want to help. I want you to be happy. I mean, I barely know you, but I *know* you. You're my sister. You're family. And I don't want you to cry. Our parents don't want you to cry. So how can I help? Tell me how to help.

(ARI stomps, pulls his/her hair in frustration:)

I wish I you'd just tell me how to help! Arrgh!

(noticing something)

Hey. Hey! Did you just laugh? Did you find that funny? Well, okay, then...

(Stomps and pulls hair again:)

I wish I could have gummy bears for dinner! Arrgh! And brush my teeth with ice cream! Arrrrrrgh!

(notices something, pleasantly surprised)

Hey. You know, Lee, you're actually kinda fun.

STOP

Taylor, very frustrated, interrupts his/her father.

TAYLOR

Stop! Just STOP, Dad! Stop talking about the "big game" that was on last night. Stop pretending that I want to know what's for dinner when I ask "What's going on?" Stop acting like everything's the same. It's not. Something's wrong. I can tell. I just can't tell *what's* wrong. You and Mom won't talk to me about it and it just, it makes the whole thing worse. For all I know, someone's really sick. Or moving across the country. Or...or...I dunno! Because you won't talk to me! It's like, it's like when I thought there were monsters under my bed, so you gave me a flashlight and had me check for myself. And I found that cockroach. Which was gross. Like *really* gross. But not as bad as monsters. So please. Tell me what's wrong. Because right now, all I see are monsters.

MULTIVERSE

Max responds to his/her science teacher, Mr. Khan.

MAX

That is an excellent question, Mr. Khan, and I will answer you in just a moment. But first, I'd like to tell you about a little something called the multiverse. As my favorite science teacher, I thought you'd want to know. It's this idea that there are millions of universes, each one with its own galaxy, its own Earth, and its own you. Yes, YOU, Mr. Khan! And all those you's, they each made different choices. Some of them probably went to college for interpretative dance. Others became influencers and shaved off their eyebrows while live-streaming. One of them probably moved to the North Pole to study the flight patterns of penguins - because that Mr. Khan lives on an Earth where penguins can fly! Isn't that cool?! To know that there are so many you's, that you have done everything you ever wanted to do!

Aaanyway, to get back to your question, the me on this Earth may not have done my homework - but! - I can guarantee that in another universe, I *did* do my homework. And that's why I believe you can mark it down as complete!

POWER

Blair enters slowly, stunned by his/her own power.

BLAIR

I did it. I lied. I actually lied. To my *mom*. I told her I did my math homework, even though I didn't solve a single problem. I didn't know I could lie like that! I didn't know I had such... such...*power*. She didn't think, even for a second, that I was lying. She trusted every word that came out of my mouth.

(realizing)

...She trusted me. And I took that trust and used it against her. Now, every time Mom looks at me, she'll think she's looking at her sweet, honest, little Blair. But really? She'll be looking into the eyes of a *liar*. Someone she doesn't even know anymore.

(scared)

Wait. I don't want that! I don't want Mom to not know me! That sounds *awful!*

(calling out)

M-Mom! I have something to tell you!

(Blair runs off.)

SUPERPOWER

Geri, very excited, runs onstage, talking to his/her dad.

GERI

Dad! I have an answer! In class today, Mr. Costello asked the students what superpower we'd want, and I couldn't decide. But now, I know: I'd fly. I'd fly over the whole, entire planet. I'd land on the tippy-top of the Eiffel Tower. Soar underneath the Niagara Falls. And glide above China - I hear they got a wall that's pretty great. But you wanna know the best part? I wouldn't be flying alone. I'd take you with me! You and Mom. Because I know it's important that you travel for work. But I...I just wish we could go with you. See all the countries you get to see. And just spend more time with you. If I could fly, then we could always be together, no matter where you go. So, yeah. That's the superpower I'd want. Pretty cool, right?

MR. FLUFFYKINS

Snowball, an intense cat, stands next to his/her fellow-cat, Mr. Fluffykins, as he/she talks to a lamp.

SNOWBALL

Hey, you. Yeah, you. My associate, Mr. Fluffykins, and I see you. Standing there. Looking so smug. What, you think just because you can brighten a whole room, that makes you better than us? Well, listen, bud, and listen close: over the course of our nine lives, we've met so many lamps just like you, we can't even keep count. You're a dime a dozen. Our mom could visit her best friend, Ikea, and come back with eleven more just like you. Now, can you guess what cats like us do with lamps like you? We push 'em. We push 'em real good. Right off the table. And you know what happens after we push 'em? ...Well. You're about to find out. So? Any last words?

(waits for a moment, then chuckles)

The silent type. You and every other lamp we ever met. Alright, bud, safe travels.

(Snowball goes to push the lamp - but at the very last moment, sees something surprising.)

Oh no, Mom's coming!

(to the lamp)

This conversation never happened. Understood?

(to Mr. Fluffykins)

Quick, Mr. Fluffykins, hide in Mom's plants!

(And with that, Snowball runs offstage.)

FAMILY

Adrian talks to his/her best friend, Finn.

ADRIAN

It's not true, Finn. I don't care how who says that family is something you're born into. They're *wrong*. It's more than that. It's...it's a feeling. That I wanna take care of someone. And they wanna take care of me. It's knowing that there are no secrets between us. None. And that we'll figure stuff out, even when it's hard. *That's* family...You're not just my best friend. You' re not just the one person I trust with all my secrets. You're family, Finn. You deserve someone that will always be there for you, and you got that. Right here.

ROUGH!

Hoagie - a dog - greets his/her human.

HOAGIE

Oh, oh! Thank goodness you're home! Lemme tell you, today has been ROUGH!

(barking)

Rough! Rough!

(not barking)

First, I thought I was being followed! Yes, FOLLOWED! All the way from the kitchen floor to the kitchen window! Every time I turned around, I saw something try to hide right behind me. So, I chased it! I chased it around and around for hours! It was rough!

(barking)

Rough! Rough!

(not barking)

But finally, I caught it! Between my teeth! I bit down REAL hard! And that's when I realized...it was my own tail! Can you believe that?! But that's not even the ROUGHEST thing that happened today! I got SO much more to tell you!

(Hoagie sees her human go to leave the room.)

Hey, hey, hey, where are you going? You haven't given me pets yet! You can't leave without petting my scruff!

(barking)

Scruff! Scruff, scruff! SCRUFF!!!!

RAINBOWS

Charley speaks to his/her friend, Em.

CHARLEY

You know what, Em? People are obsessed with rainbows. Like, *obsessed*. The moment a rainbow appears, everyone's like, "Whoa, this rainbow makes those cliffs look gorgeous! I need to take a picture!" But the thing is, *the cliffs were already gorgeous.* Full of beauty and wonder just waiting to be seen. They may not be as obvious without a rainbow, but that doesn't mean they're not there.

(Charley points.)

Like there, the old, broken swing my dad and I used to play on? It's full of laughter and joy and a hundred beautiful moments. And if I can see that, then why can't my dad-

(corrects himself/herself)

I mean, why can't people *like* my dad see all the beauty already around them, without a shiny, new rainbow to make them pay attention? That's all I'm saying.

(after a moment)

I'm really gonna miss this house. I know my dad keeps saying I'll love the new place once I get there. That it's got a big, beautiful backyard and we'll even build a new swing. But I like *this* backyard. I love this swing, even if it is broken. There's beauty right here. I only wish he could see it.

SORRY

Jesse speaks to his/her best friend, Jo, who is very upset.

JESSE

I'm sorry, Jo. Okay? I'm sorry. I just, I thought it was a funny picture. It made me laugh. And I thought it would make others laugh, too. But not in a way that would hurt you. I *never* meant to hurt you. I deleted the pic once I realized how upset you were, but by then, Ash had already screen-capped it and shared it with all his friends, and then they shared it with all *their* friends. It all happened so fast. If I could take it back, I would. I really would. But I can't. So, can we just pretend like it never happened? Please?

(after a moment)

Come on, Jo, talk to me. You're my best friend. You're...my only friend. And if I don't have you, I don't know what I'll do.

(after another moment)

Jo?

CRUSH

[NOTE: Pronouns can be changed to accommodate the actor playing the role.]

Robin talks to her friend.

ROBIN

I don't get it. I don't get why people call liking someone "having a crush." To crush something means to squish it. To flatten it. And that doesn't sound nice at all. But a crush? Having a crush is the best feeling in the whole world! When I think about...

(doesn't say the name)

Well, let's just say a certain someone. When I think about that certain someone, I can't help but smile from ear to ear, like two invisible fairies are pulling at my cheeks. And when I see that certain someone walking down the hallway, I find myself skipping all the way to class. And when I'm eating lunch in the cafeteria and he decides for the first time ever to sit across from me, I feel my heartbeat thumping between my ears, so loud that I can't even hear what he's saying.

(more and more stressed)

And then I realize that's he stopped talking and is just staring at me, so he's probably waiting for me to respond, but I have no idea what he said, so I don't wanna say something that makes him think I was just ignoring him, and I dunno what to do, but the longer I can't decide what to do, the more I can see him thinking that this was a mistake, and I feel this weight in my chest, this heavy, heavy weight, like I'm being squished-

(stops, realizing)

Ooooooooh, now I get it.

GONE

Harley runs on, panicked.

HARLEY

Dad! Dad! It's gone! It's just - gone! I'd just finished building it and went for a quick swim, so when I came back and didn't see it, I thought I musta swam further than I meant to, but then I saw you sitting here wearing your *totally* embarrassing pink flamingo shorts, and I knew I was in the right spot. So I checked again, but still couldn't find my sand castle anywhere! Like it never existed at all. Like all my work was for nothing!

(a new thought)

Wait a minute. Do...do you think this is how Mom feels when she spends hours making us dinner, goes into the kitchen to grab more napkins, and by the time she comes back, we've already eaten everything? Maybe I should eat slower. And build sand castles further from the water.

INSULT

Parker, horrified, speaks to his/her best friend.

PARKER

Why?! Why would she do this to me?! Mom is supposed to love me, to protect me, to make sure I'm happy. Why would she ever, EVER pack me a salad?! This isn't lunch. This is an insult! What did I do to deserve this? Did I offend her? Did I leave a red crayon in my pocket when my pants went in the wash again? Did I forget her birthday? I mean, Mom must have had, like, a hundred birthdays, so what if I miss one?

(Parker notices something: a note.)

Hey, she included a note. Well, let's see what she has to say for herself.

(reads the note)

"Parker, you know that recently I've been trying to eat better. And since I always feel stronger when you're with me, I thought it would be nice if we did this together. Love, Mom."

(all anger gone)

Oh...Well, okay, I guess I can do this. For Mom.

(Picks up a fork. Preparing for it...)

Here we go.

(Takes a bite out of the salad. After a moment:)

...Mmmm. So good.

FRIEND

Piper, uncomfortable, approaches his/her friend, Reed.

PIPER

Hey, Reed? I, uh, I gotta talk to you about something. I've been meaning to talk to you about it for, um, a while, but every time I'm about to, I think, "Now's not a good time." Because there, well, there is no good time. But still, I gotta say it...The way you talk about my sister, when you say she's a loser and that she doesn't have any friends and that you can't believe I'm related to her...I...I want you to stop. If you're still gonna be my friend, I *need* you to stop. I don't wanna lose you, I really don't, but I can't listen to you anymore. She's already having a rough time - like, *really* rough - and she doesn't need you, ya know, adding to it. She...she cries. Every night. I hear her. Crying through my bedroom wall. Crying herself to sleep. She doesn't deserve that. And not just because she's my sister. Because she's my friend. And I hope you will be, too. But...but that's up to you.

FINE

Terry tries to hide his/her stress.

TERRY

Mom, I'm not freaking out. I'm totally not. It's fine, it's totally fine that Wren and Max are becoming friends. They're both my friends, they have been for years, and nothing's gonna change that. Nothing. So what if they're hanging out without me? That's cool, that's totally cool. We're gonna be outta town anyway, celebrating GiGi's birthday. It's not every day my great-grandma turns ninety-five, so I couldn't join them even if I wanted to. And I don't, I totally don't. It's not like they're gonna hang out and realize that they like each other so much more than me and both decide to stop being my friends.

(laughing too loud)

HAHAHA that would be ridiculous! No WAY that's gonna happen! This is fine. It's totally, absolutely, one-hundred-thousand-percent fine.

(For a moment, Terry actually looks calm. But then:)
Look, I know it's GiGi's ninety-fifth birthday, but can I just send her a card instead?!

MULTIFACETED

Madison talks to his/her classmate, Stevie.

MADISON

Stevie, who cares if I like dolls and action figures? I like lotsa stuff. My mom says I'm "multifaceted." Multifaceted enough to know that nothing is just one thing. Like my action figure, The Annihilator. After a day spent beating bad guys, even The Annihilator wants to relax. My mom calls it "indulging in some self-care." So, The Annihilator goes and gets its razor-sharp claws manicured with my doll, Sweet Stacy. Then they get massages from Teddy T. Bear, master masseuse and the fluffiest bear in five miles. Cuz The Annihilator gets that it's not just a fighting machine from the planet Chaotica. It is a *multifaceted* fighting machine that knows nothing is more important than annihilating stress. Now, do you have any other questions, Stevie, or can Sweet Stacy and The Annihilator get back to their "restorative yoga" class?

OUT OF SIGHT

Hayden talks to his/her friend, Nicky.

HAYDEN

That's not true, Nicky. I do care about you. I do. I just...I'm not good at...

> *(Hayden's struggling, not sure how to put it. Then, an idea:)*

The first time my dad took me out on his boat, we went way, way out. Miles into the ocean. The motor was loud enough that we pretended we couldn't talk over it, but even if it had been silent, we wouldn't have said a word to each other. Finally, Dad turned off the engine and pointed out at the water and said, "What do you see, Hayden?" I shrugged. "Uh, the ocean?" He shook his head. "Look, Hayden. Really look." So, I looked. I stared at the water for minutes. Until, finally, I saw something move, just beneath the surface. Plants like nothing I'd ever seen. Fish of every shape and color. An entire world just out of sight. But it was there. Always there...I'm sorry, Nicky. That I'm not better at showing how I feel. But I hope you believe me when I say those feelings are there. They always will be. Just beneath the surface.

ROTTEN

Shea talks to his/her mom.

SHEA

I dunno, Mom. I'm all for getting in the Halloween spirit, but making Jack-o'-lanterns out of pumpkins is a little cliché, don't you think? Besides, there's nothing scary about pumpkins. But you wanna know what fruit is scary? Avocados. One minute, they're nice and fresh, then the next - BAM! - rotten. Like a pack of round, little zombies staring at you from the kitchen counter. Terrifying. They're what we should be using to make our Jack-o'-lanterns. And if that means that we don't get to eat avocados for a while, well, that's a sacrifice I'm willing to make.

GOODBYE

Brooklyn talks to his/her foster dog, Diesel.

BROOKLYN

They're good people. And they're gonna take such good care of you, Diesel. You'll be so happy, your tail won't stop wagging for years, I just know it.

(after a moment)

Please don't look at me like that. Mom and Dad made it super clear that we were only fostering you. So you could learn enough to be a good boy and find your forever home. And you did. You did it, boy. I'm so happy for you. And so...so sad. Sad that I won't get to go on runs with you anymore. Or give you scritchy-scratches until your leg's moving so fast that it's just a blur. I'm so happy and so sad at the same time. I didn't even know that was possible. I guess we both learned something, huh? Goodbye, Diesel. You really are a good boy.

WEREWOLF

Rylan stands at his/her locker, talking to a friend, Skye.

RYLAN

Skye, I'm telling you, Mr. Hill is a werewolf. How else do you explain the patchy hair on his face and bags under his eyes? Plus, he teaches chemistry. *Chemistry!* If I was a werewolf, the first thing I'd do is study chemistry to see if I could develop a potion to cure myself - and that is exactly what Mr. Hill is doing! He-
(sees something, an urgent whisper)
He's coming this way, Mr. Hill is coming this way, act natural!
(Rylan tries to "act natural", watching Mr. Hill walk by.)
Good morning, Mr. Hill. Can't wait for class this after-moon.
(realizes the mistake)
Noon! After*noon*. Who said anything about a moon? Not me. Aaaaanyway, seeya moon-
(corrects again)
SOON! See you SOON, Mr. Hill.
(Rylan watches Mr. Hill walk away.)
Did you see that, Skye? That look Mr. Hill gave me, as if I was the weird one? Well, that's *exactly* what a werewolf would do if he wanted to make us doubt our suspicions. Yeah, he's totally a werewolf. Totally, totally a werewolf.

SNOWMAN

Aster speaks to his/her mom.

ASTER

Mom, did you get the carrot? And the pink-and-blue scarf?
> *(Aster takes the carrot and scarf from his/her mom.)*

Thanks.
> *(During the below, Aster puts the finishing touches on the snowman...)*

It's weird. Making a snowman without Grandma. Remember how she'd knit a new scarf every year, so each snowman would feel special? Still, I'm glad we're re-using one of the ones she knitted. And pink and blue were always her favorite.
> *(after a moment)*

I keep wondering. Where is this snowman gonna go when spring comes? I know it's gonna melt, but I...I dunno, I don't think that's the end. I think about all the water that makes up my snowman, and how it will go where all water goes: to the ocean. And once it's in the ocean, it won't just be a melted snowman anymore. It will be so much more than that. It's gonna be the tides. The crashing of the waves. It will be a part of *every* snowman that ever melted. And it will never be alone.
> *(Takes a step back and looks at the finished snowman.)*

I like it. I bet Grandma would, too.

REVOLUTION

Everest stands up in class and speaks to his/her teacher, Mrs. Pico.

EVEREST

A pop quiz? Are you serious, Mrs. Pico?! Talk about history repeating itself! How did we feel the last time you sprang a pop quiz on us? Bad. And how do we feel now? REALLY bad! So, I, for one, am taking a lesson from the great revolutionists and boycotting this quiz! As Ben Franklin once said...well, I dunno what he said, cuz I didn't do the assigned reading. BUT STILL! Who's with me?!

> *(Everest looks at the class and realizes no one else is raising their hands.)*

Anybody? No?

> *(to Mrs. Pico)*

You win this round, Mrs. Pico. But who knows? The next time there's a pop quiz, maybe I'll make history.

THINKING

Indie speaks to his/her dad.

INDIE

Dad, I gotta tell you something. I've been thinking about it a lot - like, a *lot* - and I don't wanna play this year. I know how much you love coaching, and I like being coached by you, but I...I don't like baseball. At least, not enough to practice every day. Running the same drills, losing sleep over how we're gonna do in the playoffs. It's not how I want to spend my time. What I want to do is draw. Whenever I hold a bat, I just wish I was holding a pen. And I don't lose sleep over what I'm gonna draw. Because every time I dream, I think up a new creature or world that I'm so excited to put on the page. I'm sorry I waited so long to tell you. I just, I knew you'd be disappointed. But I want you to know that even though I don't like baseball, I'm so glad we got to spend all that time together...and I hope you are, too.

HERO

Francis approaches his/her drama teacher, Ms. Kelly.

FRANCIS

Excuse me, Ms. Kelly? I think there's been a mistake. Your cast list for the school play? It says I've been cast as the hero. But I play the villain. I *always* play the villain. It's what I do. Do you remember when you cast me as the angry cave troll? The moment I came downstage and bellowed at the audience...

(bellows ferociously)

The entire kindergarten class cried in unison! Or how about when I played the evil demon whose laugh could turn hearts to stone? I spent *months* perfecting that laugh, and can still do it. Just watch.

(laughs maniacally)

See?! I know how to play the villain. I know how to make audiences fear me and hate me, all at the same time. I know how to make them boo for me. But I *don't* know how to play the hero. I don't know if I *can* play the hero. It's not that I don't want to. But what if it turns out that audiences will *only* boo for me? What if I can't make them root for me? What if...what if nobody roots for me?

SUGAR

Remi, in the midst of a huge sugar rush, sits in the passenger seat as his/her mom drives the car.

REMI
Thank you, Mom! Thank you, thank you, THANK you for driving me! I couldn't wait another MINUTE to go to The Sugar Shack. I'm almost out of the five pounds of chocolate I bought last week, and if I run out, I dunno WHAT I'll do. Seriously, you're a life saver. OH! I should get some Lifesavers! You know, those little, round sugar candies that make my mouth tingle for hours? Yeah, yeah, yeah, I'll get some Lifesavers, SEVEN pounds of chocolate, four Marshmallow Fluffs, and two Fizzy Pixie Sticks!

(Remi looks out the car window.)

Mom, what's taking so long? We should be at The Sugar Shack by now.

(realizes something)

Wait a second. This isn't the way to The Sugar Shack. This is the way to...

(absolute horror)

THE DENTIST?!?!

GOLD

Eden comes in to talk to his/her younger sister, Rowan.

EDEN

Hey, Rowan? I, uh, I wanted to talk to you for a sec, if that's cool. I, um, I know you're disappointed. You worked so hard - just, *so* hard - preparing for that spelling bee, how can you not be bummed? But there's, you know, there's no shame in third. That's bronze. That still means you, um...what's the word?...*placed*. Top three.

(realizes he/she's gotten off-track)

But that's not what I wanted to say. Sorry, I'm not very good at, um, at this sort of thing.

(takes a deep breath)

What I wanted to say is, you may be my little sister, but you...you've done things I can't even imagine. I'm not good at speaking in front of, well, *anyone*. But there you were, competing in front of the whole school. I couldn't believe it. I just, I was so scared for you. But more than that, I was...impressed. So impressed by you. It was the coolest thing I've ever seen. And the bravest. You were braver than I've ever been. And in my book, that's...well, that's gold.

PAINTINGS

Jude talks to his/her mom.

JUDE

I just wanna warn you, Mom, your birthday presents are a little different this year. Because *you* made them. I can explain. Remember when Dad made me clean the attic? Well, I found your paintings. The ones that *you* painted. At first, I was just confused. I didn't know you could paint! Dad said you don't like to talk about it, because you "left it in the past," and, okay, I get that you don't paint anymore, but I don't get why the *paintings* have to stay in the past. I mean, they're still here. And even covered in dust and cobwebs, they're maybe the prettiest things I've ever seen. So...So, I cleaned them. And got them framed. See?

(Jude shows the paintings.)

They're your birthday presents, so you can do what you want with them, but I hope you hang them up down here. I want everyone to see what you made. They're so cool, Mom. And so are you.

MIDDLE CHILD

Harper stands outside, waiting to be picked up from karate class.

HARPER

It's fine, it's totally fine. So what if Dad's late? He probably just got stuck in traffic and will be here any minute to pick me up. Yeah, yeah, any minute. I mean, karate class only got out ten minutes ago, so it's not like I've been *abandoned* or anything. It's not like he's just forgotten about me. It's not like it's totally easy to forget that I, the middle child, even exist, until it's midnight and Dad's like, "I feel like I forgot something. Was it to pick up milk? Or the dry cleaning? NOPE! It was my CHILD, Harper!" Oh, who am I kidding?! That's exactly what happened! I have been completely forgotten! They'll move on, and I'll never see my family ever again!!!

(Harper notices something.)

Dad? Hey! I didn't see you parked over there. I hope I didn't keep you waiting.

SIT

Ellis talks to his/her dog, Rufus.

ELLIS

You know what? We're studying Greek mythology in English class, and one thing that doesn't get talked about NEARLY enough is how hard it must have been for Hades to train Cerberus. Sure, Hades is the god of the Underworld, but getting a three-headed dog to not bark through the whole night seems like a HERCULEAN task. Cuz you, Rufus, may only have one head, but you're STILL impossible! You won't even sit! I've given you POUNDS of treats. I've petted your belly for hours. I even made you a bed out of my favorite t-shirts! So, WHY?! Why won't you listen to me?!

(realizing)

I'm getting upset. I'm sorry, Rufus, it's not your fault that you don't understand. I just need a break before we keep training. I'm gonna go sit down.

(Ellis sees something miraculous.)

Hey. Hey! Did you...did you just SIT?! You did! You just SAT! Good boy, Rufus! Such a good, good boy!

(very relieved)

Oh, thank Zeus.

MINE

Maddox is very frustrated.

MADDOX

No, Mom! No! I don't want any more of Avery's old jeans! Or
Camden's old shirts! Just cuz I'm the youngest doesn't mean my
ENTIRE WARDROBE should be handed down to me! Most of my
clothes are older than I am! Can't I have ONE t-shirt that doesn't
have a hole in the armpit? Or a SINGLE pair of pants that aren't
covered in ketchup stains? Every year, on the first day of school,
Avery always has the newest, coolest clothes. But by the time I get
them, they've been out of style for five years. And I...I know that all
this stuff costs money. But can't I have one thing - *one thing* -
that's just mine?

MOVING

Dakota records a video for his/her best friend, Morgan.

DAKOTA

Hey, Morgan. Sorry for the super random video. I know we, like, *just* hung out, but there was something I wanted to tell you and I couldn't do it. Not face-to-face. So, I thought this might be easier? But now that I'm doing it, I dunno if that's true.

(after a moment)

I still have them. Every birthday present you ever got me. All the way back to the Spider-man watch you gave me when we were five.

(Looks at the watch on his/her wrist.)

I mean, what five-year-old gets their friend a *watch?* But that's what I love about you. You always surprise me. When I'm with you, I never know what to expect. And I'm just...I'm gonna miss you so much.

(difficult to say)

My mom got a new job. She's super excited. Like, I've *never* seen her so excited. But it's, um, it's far. Really, really far. And I'm just, I'm so mad. And sad. That I won't get to see you every day. That you won't get to surprise me every day. That it won't be the same. It won't ever be the same again.

(a deep breath, calming down)

But that's the great thing about you, Morgan. No day with you has ever been the same. And maybe this is just another surprise. Maybe you'll come up with a thousand new ways to surprise me. And maybe I'll finally think up some ways to surprise you. And maybe...maybe it won't feel like we lost anything at all.

TREEHOUSE

Jett approaches his/her mom.

JETT

Hey, Mom? I know you just finished building my treehouse. And it looks great. So cool. But...do you think you could build it again? Just closer to the ground? Or, you know, *on* the ground? I guess I didn't think about how high up it would be. I mean, I know it's called a "treehouse," but couldn't that be, like, a house *inside* a tree? And *not* on top of it? But, hey, other than that, it looks amazing! So, yeah, if you could just take the whole thing down and re-build it on the grass, I think we'd have something really special. Thanks!

GRANDPA

Kade talks to his/her grandfather.

KADE

Hi, Grandpa. Sorry it's been a while, but it's been raining a lot. I'm glad I finally got to visit, cuz there's something I need to talk about. And I just, I can't talk about it with anyone at home. Jason's my little brother, he looks up to me, you know? And Mom and Dad are who I need to talk about, so I can't exactly tell them how I feel. But you? I know you'll listen.

(takes a deep breath)

Mom and Dad have been fighting. A lot, even for them. For weeks now. They don't do it in front of me and Jason. At dinner, it's silent. Like, completely silent. Then they get up, wash the dishes, and go to their room. As soon as the door closes, it starts. The yelling. The crying. The anger. So, so much anger. And even though it's not in front of us, Jason and I hear it. And feel it. Like all that anger has filled the house. And we're drowning in it...Last night, Jason asked me if they're gonna split up. I didn't know what to say. Part of me is terrified that they will. But another part of me thinks that it's the best thing that could happen. Cuz then it would be over. The fighting would stop. The anger would be gone. And we could breathe again. Finally breathe.

(after a moment)

Thanks for listening, Grandpa. I know you can't offer any advice, but it feels good to actually *talk* about it, you know? Oh! I almost forgot - I brought you some more flowers. Daisies this time. I know I usually bring lilies, since those are the only flowers Mom knows for sure you liked, but I dunno, I thought a change might be nice. I hope you like them.

(Kade places the flowers down on his/her grandfather's grave.)

I should go. But now that the rain's stopped, I'll be back soon. I promise. Bye, Grandpa.

A NEW CHAPTER

Pat speaks to his/her teddy bear, Barry (Barry can either be unseen or an actual teddy bear held by Pat).

PAT

Listen, Barry, you've been great. Really, just the best. But we both knew this couldn't last forever. Don't think of this as the end, but as the start of a new chapter. Being put on sale will be the best thing that ever happened to you. Some little kid's gonna come to Mom's yard sale, see you sitting there, and realize you're the teddy bear he's always needed.

(after a moment)

Don't look at me like that, Barry. Please. I know you think I'm doing this so I can buy the latest phone, but it's not that simple. I'm not a little kid anymore. I'm a big kid who needs big toys. Like a new phone. So what if you were my first real friend? So what if you cuddled me to sleep every night? So what if you're the best teddy bear a kid could ask for? None of that matters. Cuz I...I...

(unable to go through with it)

I can't do this! I can't lose you! I'll sell my bed if I have to, but not you, Barry! Never you!

SUMMER SCHOOL

Teegan speaks to his/her teacher, Miss Gorlow.

TEEGAN

Summer school?! No, no, no, I can't go to summer school, Miss Gorlow! I can't help it that I'm not good at math. Besides, I already have a billion plans for the summer. Jay and I are gonna go swimming. Then when I hang out with Alex, we're...also gonna go swimming. But then, when I hang out with Lee, we'll...probably go to the beach and may or may not go swimming. Okay, so I may not have a *billion* plans, but still, I can't go to summer school. Cuz if I go, everyone will know. Jay. Alex. Lee. They'll know that I'm...I'm not as smart as them. And I don't want that. I don't want that at all. I just want to swim. So, what do you say, Miss Gorlow - will you let me swim?

BRAIN FREEZE

Sunny speaks to his/her best friend, Ellie.

SUNNY

That's a great question, Ellie, and I am thrilled to tell you why I spent all my lunch money on ice cream sandwiches. It's cuz I'm *[actual age]* now. Pretty much an adult. Which means I get to do whatever I want. So when Mom tells me not to eat an ice cream sandwich too quickly or I'll get brain freeze, I make the very adult decision to prove her wrong - by eating *five* ice cream sandwiches in less than a minute. I want the world to know what I accomplished here today, so I need you to time me, starting - NOW!

> *(Sunny eats an ice cream sandwich very quickly. While chewing...)*

One down, four to go!

> *(Starts to eat a second ice cream sandwich - but after just a few bites, gets hit with a MASSIVE brain freeze. Tries to hide it...)*

OW! I mean - *wow!* Wow, that is good.

> *(the brain freeze gets worse)*

Wow-wow-wow, I can barely HANDLE how GOOD that is!!!

> *(Sunny goes to take another bite, but changes his/her mind.)*

You know, it's SO good that I don't wanna rush it. I wanna take my time and enjoy it. And I think you should, too, Ellie. Here. Have three ice cream sandwiches.

> *(Sunny hands Ellie the three remaining ice cream sandwiches, then starts to exit.)*

Hey, I think I left my phone in the locker-room, I'll be right back.

> *(Running off:)*

AHHHHHH, SO COLD!!!!!!!!!!!!

COOKING

Lane talks to his/her parents.

LANE

Mom, Dad, sit down. You both work so hard that I wanted to do something special for you. So, I made dinner! Now, you may be wondering, "How did our Lesley become a master chef in one day?" And the answer is, of course, TikTok. I watched a hundred cooking videos, so I know what I'm doing. I learned that the most important rule of cooking is to "make it work!" NOW! The first course! I have prepared a-

(trying to say "charcuterie")

-charred-koosh-er-y board.

(Lane presents the charcuterie board.)

I know how proud you get when you make one for your friends, so I had no idea it'd be so easy! I still had a slice of ham in my lunchbox, so I just scraped the jelly off my PB&J, and added in some string-cheese that I found in my pocket. See? Easy!

(Sets the board down in front of them.)

Go on, don't be shy.

(after a moment)

Not hungry? Or are you just saving room for the main course? Good call! Because you're about to have a real treat: "Lesley's Legendary Lasagna!" The recipe is super simple. It's two cans of Spaghetti-o's, six slices of whole-wheat bread, sixteen ounces of ketchup, and the other half of the string-cheese from my pocket.

(Lane watches his/her mom and dad stand up and head to the kitchen.)

Hey, where are you going? You're gonna miss desert!

MATH

[NOTE: Pronouns can be changed to accommodate the actor playing the role.]

Dominique speaks directly to the audience.

DOMINIQUE

I don't just like math. I *live* for math. With math, the world makes sense. One plus one always equals two. Twenty-nine minus eleven always equals eighteen. If you take that eighteen and multiply it by seven, you will always get one-hundred-and-twenty-six. *Always.* Math is consistent. Certain. It brings me comfort. At least, it did. Until the new kid came to class. Ellis. Deep, ocean-blue eyes. The brightest smile. And his laugh? I could live inside his laugh forever.

(Dominique shakes her head, horrified.)

Ugh, did you hear that!? "I could live inside his laugh forever?!" That doesn't even make any sense! But that's the sort of nonsense I've been thinking ever since he showed up! I tried to do my homework, but when I got to the question, "What is eight multiplied by six?" Rather than writing "forty-eight" like a NORMAL PERSON, I just drew a little heart! A HEART! Math is NUMBERS, it has nothing to do with hearts! With math, one plus one ALWAYS equals two!

(a realization)

One plus one always equals two. One *plus* one. What if...what if Ellis and I are just a math problem that needs to be solved? Maybe we're two one's standing next to each other, waiting for someone to do the math. Well, if anyone can do it, it's me.

(determined)

I'm gonna ask Ellis on a date. I like my odds.

DUNGEON MASTER

Finn, a Dungeon Master, talks to his/her adventuring party.

FINN

You want me to jump right into the recap? You're sure there's nothing you want to say, or maybe celebrate, before we get into tonight's D&D session? Like - oh, I dunno - a certain *Dungeon Master's* birthday?...No? Well. Alright, then.

(clears throat)

So. To recap. You're an adventuring party that's been on lots of really cool adventures that you probably wouldn't have survived without the help of a kind and benevolent DM who may or not be turning *[insert your age]* very soon. MOVING ON! To tonight's adventure! I...You know what?...I had this whole arc planned where you were gonna go meet a herd of baby owlbears and pet their cute little bellies - but NOT! ANYMORE! Instead, as you all leave "Penelope's Pickled Potion Pantry," FIFTEEN FLAME SKULLS POUNCE ON YOUR HEADS! But before you can even roll initiative, FIFTY KRAKENS pop out of a sewer grate! And last - but oh-ho-ho, certainly not least! - a FULL-ON ANCIENT RED DRAGON nose-dives out of the clouds to unleash its WRATH upon you! It bellows in its native tongue.

(bellows like a dragon)

But unfortunately, none of you speak Draconic, so you don't understand that it's saying, "You should have remembered your DM's birthday!" Alriiiiiight, NOW you can roll initiative!

PROMISE

Tristan looks into the crib of his/her baby brother, Wren.

TRISTAN

So. You're my baby brother. Wren. Smaller than I expected.
Smellier, too. But that's okay…I know you can't speak yet. Maybe
you can't even understand me, I dunno. But still, I wanna make
you a promise. And when you can speak, I'm gonna ask you to
make it, too. Okay, here goes…
   (clears throat)
I promise to never tell our parents when you sneak an extra scoop
of ice cream after dinner. Or don't do your homework until we're
on the bus to school. I promise that you can always come into my
room and play music as loud as you want. Or video games. Or
whatever you need to play to drown out all the fighting. I promise
to warn you when Dad's in one of his moods. And when Mom
"needs some space." I promise that you won't ever have to tip-toe
around me. That you will never feel completely alone. And I
promise - I *promise* - that we will get through this. Together.

ALWAYS

Dallas talks to his/her cat, Tigger.

DALLAS

I know, Tigger. I know you're in pain. But I don't care what Mom says, or what the vet says, or what *anyone* says. I don't believe that there's only one option. I *can't* believe it. I can't believe that I won't fall asleep with you purring on my chest. I can't believe that I won't wake up to you meowing for breakfast. I can't believe that my best friend will be gone. I can't.

(after a moment)

...But...I see how much pain you're in. I see how much it's hurting you to even breathe. And if I keep you here just cuz I'm not ready to lose you, then...then *I'm* the one who's hurting you. And I never want to hurt you, Tigger, not ever. Even if it means...

(Dallas makes a decision. Calls offstage:)

Hey, Mom. I think we should go back to the vet's. I think...I think it's time.

(Turns back to Tigger.)

Tigger. I want you to know - no, I want the *whole world* to know - that you will always be my best friend. Always.

CAMPING

Shiloh is horrified by what his/her mom just said.

SHILOH

What?! What do you mean there's no cell reception?! We're camping here for a whole WEEK, what am I supposed to do without reception?! How am I supposed to stay up-to-date on all the latest trends? Is that bush gonna show me the funniest memes? Will those trees drop TikTok videos? Is this sunset gonna give me endless lolz? No! How could you do this to me, Mom?! You've trapped me in a pop-culture wasteland, with nothing to keep me company but that bush, those trees, and this sunset.

(Shiloh looks at the sunset for a moment, surprised by its beauty.)

Wow...I didn't know sunsets could look like this. No, not just look. I didn't know they could make me *feel* like this. Warm, but on the inside. I've seen lots of sunsets online, but they've never made me feel anything...Hey, Mom? I'm sorry I yelled at you. Do you wanna sit together and watch the sun set?

THE TEAM

Penn has just found out that his/her friend, Royce, made the soccer team and he/she didn't. Penn tries to stay positive while talking to Royce.

PENN

No, hey, it's okay, Royce. Really. So what if I didn't make the team? What matters is that *you* made the team. I mean, you trained just as hard as I did. Practiced every day, just like I did. Ran drills in the pouring rain, just like I did. So, if only one of us could make the team, I'm happy that it's...I'm happy that...

(a deep breath)

No. No, you know what? I'm not gonna lie. Not to you. To tell you the truth, Royce, I'm not happy. Not at all. I'm confused. And frustrated. And disappointed. *Really* disappointed. I worked so hard. Just as hard as you. And it hurts to know Coach Thompson didn't think I was good enough. It hurts so, so much.

(after a moment)

But that doesn't mean I'm not happy for you. I'm hurting *and* I'm happy for you. And that's the truth.

GOOD BOY

Noa talks to his/her mom.

NOA

Mom, hey, don't be too mad at Dad. He only got me a puppy cuz I
wanted one so, so, *so* badly. And he really is a good boy. The
puppy, I mean. Not Dad. But the thing is, even if he's not perfect,
he's doing his best. Dad, I mean. Not the puppy. And besides, you
won't have to worry about a thing, because I'm gonna make sure
he's super well-trained. The puppy, not Dad. But hey - I'm happy
to train Dad, too, if you want.

BIKE

Julian talks to his/her friend, Eli.

JULIAN

Oh, wow, yeah, I'd love to go biking with you, Eli. I totally would.
But I can't. Because I...I...
   (lying)
I lost my bike. At the zoo. Yeah, yeah, such a bummer. I rode my
bike to the zoo cuz I *totally* love biking and I'm really, really good
at it. Obviously. But when I went to lock it up, a panda ran out of
the zoo! It was making a run for it. Or, actually, a *ride* for it. It
grabbed my bike and just - rode off! Wasn't wearing a helmet or
anything. And speaking of helmets, I lost my helmet, too. So, even
if you had an extra bike I could ride, that *still* wouldn't work. Cuz
after I walked home from the zoo, I left my helmet in its usual
spot, on the, um, helmet shelf. But the next day, it was gone. Just
gone. I think a turtle probably took it...Which, now that I've said it,
sounds pretty nuts. But I can explain.
   (struggling to think of an explanation)
I saw on the, um, Discovery Channel that turtles are always
looking for ways to strengthen their shells. Increase their defenses.
So, naturally, a turtle came wandering through my house, saw the
helmet, and thought it would make the perfect armor.
   (losing steam)
Cuz a helmet is the same shape as a...a shell.
   (a deep sigh)
I can't do this. I'm gonna be honest with you, Eli. I don't know how
to ride a bike.

EMPLOYEE OF THE MONTH

Kendall speaks to his/her dad.

KENDALL

Hey, Dad? I know it's been weird for you. Being home all the time. And that you were bummed - like, *really* bummed - for a while. And I still think your job made a *huge* mistake when they got rid of you. But that's not what I wanted to say. What I wanted to say is...it's been great. Having you home so much. It's so fun gaming with you. And I love it when you help me with my school stuff, even when we're both struggling with my math homework. And your dish-washing has come so, *so* far. That's why I want you to have this.

(Kendall holds up a piece of paper.)

I made it myself. It says, "Employee of the Month."

STORIES

Emerson sits on the train. He/she speaks directly to the audience.

EMERSON

It never gets old. Not ever. I could sit on the train forever. I wouldn't even care where I was going. Because it's not the train that's the cool part. It's the people. Everybody in the middle of stories that are still being written. Like, maybe that woman is getting ready to meet her girlfriend's parents for the first time. And that guy might be on his way to the biggest interview of his life. And the old couple over there could be heading to the airport for a vacation they've been planning for longer than I've been alive! There are so many stories happening around us all the time that we will never, ever know about. But for a moment, for a single train ride, I like to imagine them.

(a new idea)

I wonder if anyone ever imagines what my story might be. I hope they imagine something cool. Like I'm about to meet up with my best friend who I haven't seen in months and he couldn't be more excited to see me. Or that I just got back from an awesome camping trip with both my parents, and we were all so, so happy. I just hope they don't imagine the truth, that I'm-

(sees something)

Oh! This is my stop.

(Emerson exits.)

About the Author

Kerry Kazmierowicztrimm has had over 500 productions of his plays and musicals staged in 15 countries. His Off-Broadway credits include having his play WOUNDED produced at the Soho Playhouse, and writing for Rattlestick Playwrights Theatre's "Village Song Project." His work was presented at Lincoln Center and The Other Palace (UK). He has written immersive and site-specific theatre seen by thousands and was commissioned by La Jolla Playhouse to write for their "Walks of Life" audio project. He has received over four dozen awards and nominations for his writing, including having been a Finalist for the Eugene O'Neill National Playwrights Conference. Several of his shows have been published, a majority of them through Beat by Beat Press. He has a B.F.A. in Acting from Syracuse University, an M.F.A. in Musical Theatre Writing from N.Y.U. Tisch School of the Arts, and a Certificate in Video Game Writing from The Narrative Department. For more information, please visit www.kerrykaz.com.

Printed in Great Britain
by Amazon

56717382R00036